Roger McGough

When I was young, the poems I liked best were the ones that could be recited or sung. I never enjoyed 'studying' poems.

I don't suppose there can be many poets who have two gold discs on the wall!

Liverpool

I am a Commander of the British Empire and a Freeman of the City of Liverpool, but you couldn't tell by looking at me.

This is me in my group, The Scaffold. We once had a number 1 hit with a song called 'Lily the Pink'.

When my daughter, Izzy, was at school, her drama class was doing some work on one of my poems. No one really knew I was Izzy's dad. So when she had to write an essay about the poem, I wrote it for her. Her teacher gave her a low mark, because she didn't agree with what Izzy (or rather I!) had written!

KU-540-577

The Sound Collector

A stranger called this morning
Dressed all in black and grey
Put every sound into a bag
And carried them away

The whistling of the kettle
The turning of the lock
The purring of the kitten
The ticking of the clock

The popping of the toaster
The crunching of the flakes
When you spread the marmalade
The scraping noise it makes

The hissing of the frying-pan
The ticking of the grill
The bubbling of the bathtub
As it starts to fill

The drumming of the raindrops
On the window-pane
When you do the washing-up
The gurgle of the drain

The crying of the baby
The squeaking of the chair
The swishing of the curtain
The creaking of the stair

A stranger called this morning
He didn't leave his name
Left us only silence
Life will never be the same.

This is one of my favourite poems because whenever I read it I can hear children making the noises that I describe. R.McG.

3

Potato Clock

A potato clock, a potato clock
  Has anybody got a potato clock?
A potato clock, a potato clock
  Oh where can I find a potato clock?

I went down to London the other day
Found myself a job with a lot of pay
Carrying bricks on a building site
From early in the morning till late at night

No one here works as hard as me
I never even break for a cup of tea
My only weakness, my only crime
Is that I can never get to work on time

A potato clock, a potato clock
  Has anybody got a potato clock?
A potato clock, a potato clock
  Oh where can I find a potato clock?

I arrived this morning half an hour late
The foreman came up in a terrible state
'You've got a good job, but you're in for a shock,
If you don't get up at eight o'clock.'

Up at eight o'clock, up at eight o'clock
  Has anybody got up at eight o'clock?
Up at eight o'clock, up at eight o'clock
  Oh where can I find up at eight o'clock?

The Allivator

at the top.

then eat you

his back

ride upon

let you

he will

in a shop

see one

if you

allivator

Beware the

Allivator is a made-up word. Alligator, escalator and elevator, all combining to make a scary animal that lurks in the corner of large department stores.
R.McG.

5

Bully Night

Bully night
I do not like
the company you keep
The burglars and the bogeymen
who slink
while others sleep

Bully night
I do not like
the noises that you make
The creaking and the shrieking
that keep me
fast awake.

Bully night
I do not like
the loneliness you bring
the loneliness you bring
The loneliness, the loneliness
the loneliness you bring,
the loneliness you bring
the loneliness, the

The Fight of the Year

And there goes the bell for the third month
and Winter comes out of its corner looking groggy
Spring leads with a left to the head
followed by a sharp right to the body
    daffodils
    primroses
    crocuses
    snowdrops
    lilacs
    violets
    pussywillow
Winter can't take much more punishment
and Spring shows no signs of tiring
    tadpoles
    squirrels
    baalambs
    badgers
    bunny rabbits
    mad march hares
    horses and hounds
Spring is merciless
Winter won't go the full twelve rounds
    bobtail clouds
    scallywaggy winds
    the sun
    a pavement artist
    in every town

A left to the chin
and Winter's down!
    tomatoes
    radish
    cucumber
    onions
    beetroot
    celery
    and any
    amount
    of lettuce
    for dinner
Winter's out for the count
Spring is the winner!

Down
   the
      snow
         white
      page
   we
slide. From
         side
            to
               side
               we
         glide. Pass
               Obstacles
                     with
                        ease
                  Words
                     on
            skis.
         Look out.
               Here
            comes
         a
   poem
      in
         a
            hurry!

UPHILL CLIMB

Wheeeeee

Three
Two
One
go.
another
have
to
top
the
to
back

way

the

all

climb

the

is

part

boring

only

The

PLAGUE AROUND

There's a plague around
There's a plague around
In every village
And every town

With big purple spots
And the greenish ones too
There's a plague around
And it's waiting for you

There's a plague around
There's a plague around
Keep your eyes open
And don't make a sound

Or your ears will flap
And you'll start to cough
You'll sneeze and sneeze
Till your nose drops off

There's a plague around
There's a plague around
In every school
There's a playground

You'll burst out laughing
And run around
When you get into
the playground

There's a playground
There's a playground
In every school
There's a playground.

Some poems begin life as a word-doodle, others are separated off from the sound of words. 'Playground,' when I half-listened to it, sounded like 'plague around'. So I began with the plague and ended up in the playground. *R.McG.*

In case of fire

In case of fire break glass
In case of glass fill with water
In case of water fetch umbrella
In case of umbrella beware of Mary Poppins
In case of Mary Poppins switch off TV
In case of TV change channel
In case of Channel swim across
In case of cross say sorry
In case of sorry hold out arms
In case of arms lay down gun
In case of gun *Fire*
In case of fire break glass

The writer of this poem

The writer of this poem
Is taller than a tree
As keen as the North wind
As handsome as can be

As bold as a boxing-glove
As sharp as a nib
As strong as scaffolding
As tricky as a fib

As smooth as an ice-cream
As quick as a lick
As clean as a chemist-shop
As clever as a ✔

The writer of this poem
Never ceases to amaze
He's one in a million billion
(or so the poem says!)

Roger McGough
How I write

My ideas usually come when faced with the blank, sometimes hostile, stare of an empty page.

My favourite poem is always the one I am working on. When I'm writing, I'm getting to know the poem as it develops, and that's exciting. It's the process of writing that I enjoy. Whenever I start a poem I rarely know how it will end. The fun is in discovering what happens.

I tend to illustrate my poems, in fact occasionally the poem is inspired by a drawing.

Sometimes I write like this:
I use different pens and don't have a favourite. I try not to be superstitious. When writing a poem I will not use the computer until it is complete. I enjoy watching the poem change shape and keep all the crossings out and rewritten versions.

I enjoy drawing and so will often make patterns on the page using words.

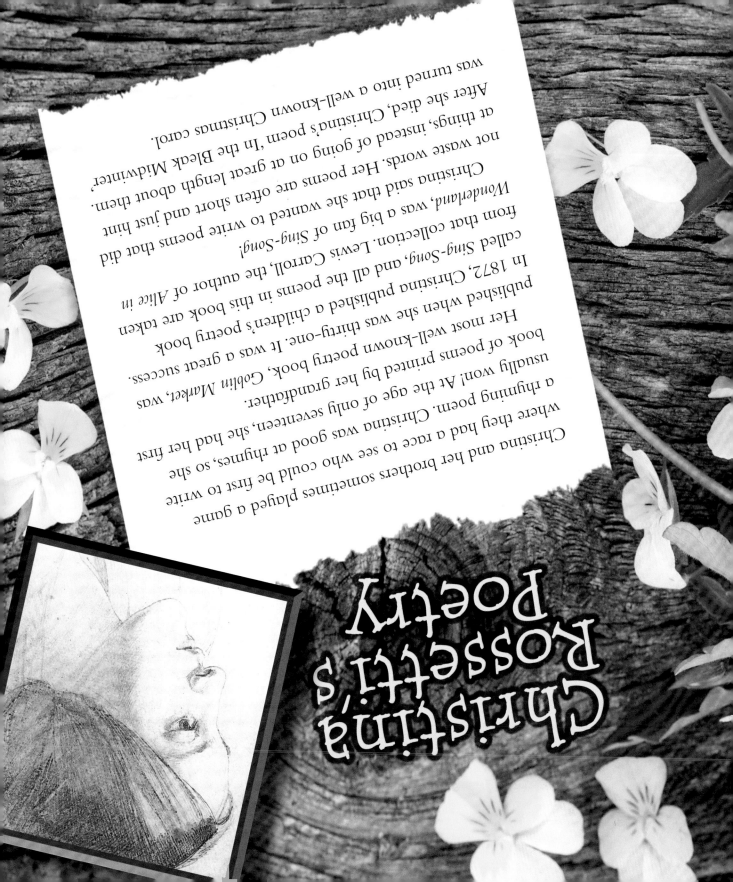

Christina Rossetti's Poetry

Christina and her brothers sometimes played a game where they had a race to see who could be first to write a rhyming poem. Christina was good at rhymes, so she usually won! At the age of only seventeen, she had her first book of poems printed by her grandfather.

Her most well-known poetry book, *Goblin Market*, was published when she was thirty-one. It was a great success. In 1872, Christina published a children's poetry book called *Sing-Song*, and all the poems in this book are taken from that collection. Lewis Carroll, the author of *Alice in Wonderland*, was a big fan of *Sing-Song*!

Christina said that she wanted to write poems that did not waste words. Her poems are often short and just hint at things, instead of going on at great length about them. After she died, Christina's poem 'In the Black Midwinter' was turned into a well-known Christmas carol.

Who Has Seen the Wind

Who has seen the wind?
    Neither I nor you:
But when the leaves hang trembling
    The wind is passing through.

Who has seen the wind?
    Neither you nor I:
But when the trees bow down their heads
    The wind is passing by.

What is Pink?

What is pink? A rose is pink
By the fountain's brink.
What is red? A poppy's red
In its barley bed.
What is blue? The sky is blue
Where the clouds float through.
What is white? A swan is white
Sailing in the light.
What is yellow? Pears are yellow,
Rich and ripe and mellow.
What is green? The grass is green,
With small flowers between.
What is violet? Clouds are violet
In the summer twilight.
What is orange? Why, an orange,
Just an orange!

What Are Heavy?

What are heavy? Sea-sand and sorrow:
What are brief? Today and tomorrow:
What are frail? Spring blossoms and youth:
What are deep? The ocean and truth.

Mix a Pancake

Mix a pancake,
Stir a pancake,
Pop it in the pan;
Fry the pancake,
Toss the pancake,
Catch it if you can.

FLINT

An emerald is as green as grass,
A ruby red as blood;
A sapphire shines as blue as heaven;
A flint lies in the mud.
A diamond is a brilliant stone,
To catch the world's desire;
An opal holds a fiery spark;
But a flint holds fire.

A flint is a hard piece of rock which creates sparks when you strike it against metal. The sparks can be used to make a fire from dry materials. So it seems as though the flint has fire inside it!

A Double Riddle

There is one that has a head without an eye,
And there is one that has an eye without a head.
You may find the answer if you try;
And when all is said,
Half the answer hangs upon a thread.

Fly Away Swallow

Fly away, fly away, over the sea,
Sun-loving swallow, for summer is done.
Come again, come again, come back to me,
Bringing the summer and bringing the sun.

Swallows are called 'sun-loving' birds because they migrate in winter to warmer places overseas. In Britain, swallows leave in September or October to fly to South Africa. When they return in April or May it's a sign that summer is coming!

Caterpillar

Brown and furry
Caterpillar in a hurry,
Take your walk
To the shady leaf, or stalk,
Or whatnot,
Which may be the chosen spot.
No toad spy you,
Hovering bird of prey pass by you;
Spin and die,
To live again a butterfly.

Hurt No Living Thing

Hurt no living thing,
Ladybird nor butterfly,
Nor moth with dusty wing,
Nor cricket chirping cheerily,
Nor grasshopper, so light of leap,
Nor dancing gnat,
Nor beetle fat,
Nor harmless worms that creep.

Daisies

Where innocent bright-eyed daisies are,
With blades of grass between,
Each daisy stands up like a star
Out of a sky of green.

Christina Rossetti

Christina Rossetti was born on 5th December 1830 in London. She had lessons at home with her parents instead of going to school. Christina was a bright, lively child. She recited her first poem to her mother at the age of six and wrote her first published poem when she was eleven!

Christina loved exploring the gardens of her grandfather's cottage, just outside London. It was on these visits that she became interested in nature. She always hated any cruelty to animals.

One of her brothers, Dante Gabriel Rossetti, became a famous painter. Christina was a beautiful young woman and was a model for some of his most well-known paintings. He also painted her portrait.

Christina never married or left home. She looked after her parents in their old age and when they were ill. Later in her life she was often very ill herself. Christina died on 29th December 1894.